Field Guide to the

Vernal Pools
of Mather Field

Sacramento County

by Carol W. Witham

California Native Plant Society
Sacramento Valley Chapter

*Dedicated to the memory of George M. Clark (1938-1996)
who inspired so many in the Sacramento Valley Chapter of
the California Native Plant Society to cherish vernal pools
and to passionately speak out for their preservation.*

Unless otherwise noted, photos, maps and illustrations
by Carol W. Witham.

© 2006 California Native Plant Society
Sacramento Valley Chapter
2707 K Street, Suite 1
Sacramento, CA 95816

ISBN: 0-943460-47-6

Printed by Commerce Printing, Sacramento, California.

Contents

About CNPS

The California Native Plant Society (CNPS) is a state-wide nonprofit organization dedicated to increasing the understanding and appreciation of California's native plants, and preserving them in their natural habitats for future generations.

CNPS carries out its mission through science, conservation advocacy, education and horticulture at the local, state, and federal levels. We monitor rare and endangered plants and habitats, act to save endangered areas through publicity, persuasion, and on occasion, legal action; provide expert testimony to government bodies; support the establishment of native plant preserves; sponsor work days to remove invasive plants; and offer a range of educational activities including speaker programs, youth learning opportunities, field trips, native plant sales, horticulture workshops, and demonstration gardens.

Since its founding in 1965, the traditional strength of CNPS has been its dedicated volunteers. CNPS activities are organized at the local chapter level where members' varied interests influence what is done.

The Sacramento Valley Chapter of CNPS covers the Sacramento, Yolo, Colusa, Sutter, Yuba, lower Placer, and northern San Joaquin County areas. We hold evening program meetings nine times a year, have a Wildflower Weekend in April, conduct two plant sales each year, and are generally active in most natural habitat and open space planning issues. Plus we are fun people with a passion about our native plants and natural areas.

Preservation of vernal pools in general, and the Mather Field vernal pools specifically, has been one of the driving forces behind our chapter leadership. In addition to continuously persuading policy makers and land use planners not to destroy the vernal pools, we have had an active public education program at the Mather Field vernal pools for the past decade.

For information and a schedule of the free spring tours at Mather Field, please contact the Sacramento Valley Chapter of the California Native Plant Society at:
916-737-WILD or
www.sacvalleycnps.org.

CNPS membership is open to all. Members receive a quarterly journal and newsletter from the state organization, plus newsletters from the local chapter. For more information about the California Native Plant Society visit: **www.cnps.org**.

About Mather Field

Mather Field is located 12 miles east of downtown Sacramento. This area was largely protected from urban and industrial development when it was commissioned as an Air Force Base in 1918. The base infrastructure occupied less than half of the 5845 acres. The rest provided a buffer around the military operations and remains relatively undisturbed.

In 1993, the base was decommissioned by the Department of Defense and the land has since been transferred to the County of Sacramento. One of the special conditions of the land transfer is that a vernal pool preserve be established and managed in perpetuity. The county and other stakeholders have been working on a plan that allows for some development while also providing for a permanent vernal pool preserve.

The California Native Plant Society is delighted that there will always be vernal pools at Mather Field for Sacramentans to visit and enjoy. We hope that with this field guide and through our guided tours, you too will come to appreciate the vernal pools at Mather Field.

A bird's eye view of the Mather Field vernal pool landscape. Photo by Tom Whitney.

What Is a Vernal Pool?

Vernal pools are temporary wetlands. They fill with water during winter rains and slowly dry down during the spring. They remain completely dry throughout the summer. Vernal pools undergo three distinct stages during each year: an aquatic phase, a flowering phase, and a drought phase. This annual cycle of flood and drought creates extreme conditions for the plants and animals that live in vernal pools.

This ephemeral stream channel is slowly cutting down into the hardpan . The rocky, cemented hardpan layer is just a foot below the soil surface. The hardpan keeps rain water perched above the soil surface and gives rise to vernal pools. Photo by Kent Valentine.

Geology and hydrology play important roles in the formation of vernal pools. Vernal pools only occur where there is the right combination of the two. The soils at Mather Field began forming millions of years ago. As rains fell on the ancient landscape, minerals such as silica and iron were dissolved from the surface layer and eventually formed a cement-like hardpan just a few inches to a few feet below the soil surface. These *hardpans* prevent rainwater from percolating downward into the subsoils. The rain water remains perched above the hardpan where it can be seen in the shallow depressions that are vernal pools. As the weather warms, the perched rain water evaporates in the sunshine, is taken up by the rapidly growing plants, or may leak through small fractures in the hardpan.

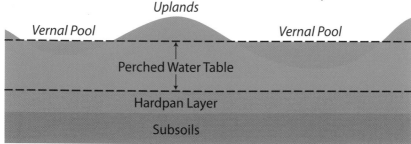

Cross section diagram showing a perched water table above the hardpan layer. This illustration is simplified. The hardpan is usually not flat or of even thickness. It may even contain cracks or holes. Hardpans often have an accumulation of clay particles on top.

Climate also plays an important role in what Californians call a vernal pool. While many places in the world support temporary rain puddles, the mass displays of vernal pool flowers only occur where there are mild wet winters and hot dry summers. This is typically known as a *Mediterranean climate*. The combination of hardpan soils and a Mediterranean climate is unique to California and a handful of other places. These special conditions have allowed many species of plants and animals to evolve and adapt to living only in California vernal pools.

Rings of vernal pool flowers in the early spring. Most of these plants grow only in California's vernal pools.
Photo by David King.

Each vernal pool is unique. This is due to both the depth to the hardpan and how long the pool remains ponded. Every year may also be different due to local rainfall amounts and patterns. This is the same pool as shown above.

Why Protect Vernal Pools?

Over 90% of California's vernal pools have already been destroyed. As you read further, you will discover that they are a unique and special home to hundreds of animals and plants that can live nowhere else. But besides saving these treasures for the creatures that inhabit them, we should save these delightful places so that future generations may also enjoy them.

Aquatic Phase

The aquatic phase of the annual vernal pool cycle begins after the first few rain storms in the late fall or early winter. Once the soils have saturated, any additional rainfall accumulates as a perched water table and the pools begin to fill. The aquatic phase lasts until the winter rainstorms have passed and warmer spring weather sets in.

Mather Field vernal pools during the peak of the aquatic phase.
Photo by Eva Butler.

To most people, the aquatic phase of a vernal pool may resemble a mud puddle, but to a variety of creatures that depend on vernal pools, it represents much more. The animals that can be found in and around vernal pools consist of three general types—those that only live in vernal pools, those that use vernal pools for part of their life cycle, and those that visit vernal pools to feed or rest. Of these general types, the animals that can only live in vernal pools are strikingly unique. Many of these species are also threatened by extinction due to past and ongoing destruction of their vernal pool habitat.

While most of the aquatic organisms that live only in vernal pools are smaller than a pinhead, several larger freshwater crustaceans—fairy shrimp, clam shrimp and tadpole shrimp—can be observed swimming and feeding. These freshwater crustaceans have evolved a very unusual adaptation to survive the extreme conditions of summer drought. They produce *cysts*. A cyst is a living embryo encased in a hard shell. This shell

Vernal Pool Fairy Shrimp (*Branchinecta lynchi*) are translucent and about a half inch long.
Photo by Larry Serpa.

California Clam Shrimp (*Cyzicus californicus*) are about the size of a dime.
Photo by David Rosen.

Vernal Pool Tadpole Shrimp (*Lepidurus packardi*) can grow to the size of a quarter or more.

helps the embryo survive the heat and dessication of summer. When the rain returns, the embryo can hatch out very quickly to begin eating, growing and reproducing. This is an advantage when your aquatic world lasts for only a few weeks.

The Western Spadefoot (Spea hammondii) breeds only in vernal pools. Their tadpoles feed on algae, plants and aquatic animals. Photo by David Rosen.

The animals that occupy vernal pools for only a part of their life cycle consist of two general categories—amphibians and insects. Both of these groups use vernal pools during their larval stage.

Amphibians mate and lay eggs in vernal pools. Their tadpoles are aquatic until they *metamorphose* into adults. Then they become terrestial until the urge to reproduce brings them back to the pools. During the late spring, you can often see young frogs, newly metamorphosed into adults on the muddy edges of the vernal pools.

The Water Scavenger Beetle (Hydrophilus sp.) is at home in vernal pools during both the larval and adult stages. The adults can be seen rising to the surface to trap air under their wings. Photo by David Rosen.

Some insects follow the same type of life cycle. They breed, usually on the wing, and then deposit their eggs in vernal pools. Their aquatic larvae are fierce predators and grow quickly due to the abundance of prey in the vernal pool aquatic ecosystem. Eventually they undergo metamorphosis and emerge as terrestrial adults able to fly off to new habitats. Some insects are great swimmers even in their adult stage. Water scavenger beetles are one example.

The aquatic phase visitors to vernal pools consist mostly of migrating waterfowl and shorebirds. They come to feast on the abundant aquatic organisms. As the aquatic phase progresses into the flowering phase, the species visiting the pools also change. Early in the season, the pools are visited by ducks and geese which feed on crustaceans and submerged plants. As the pools begin to dry, egrets and herons come to feed on small frogs, snails and insects. The muddy banks of vernal pools are a great place to look for bird footprints.

The complex food web of the aquatic vernal pool ecosystem does not end with waterfowl. Those that prey on waterfowl, their eggs and their offspring, also come to vernal pools during the aquatic phase. These predators include hawks, eagles, coyotes, badgers, snakes, and others.

Flowering Phase

Over 200 species of plants grow in California vernal pools. Of those, half are entirely restricted to this unique habitat. Plants that occur in vernal pools have several unique adaptations that allow them to survive the extremes of flood and drought. Most vernal pool plants are *annuals*, living only during the short winter and spring seasons before setting seed and dying. These plants tend to be of small stature, but with relatively large flowers. Their goal is not to grow big and survive a long time, but to reproduce and make plenty of seeds for future generations.

Checkerblooms and clovers bloom along the edge of vernal pools.

Having few leaves and very showy flowers is part of the vernal pool plants' strategy for producing abundant seed. The concentric circles, ribbons and patches of pink, yellow, white, and blue blossoms are intended to attract their pollinators. While many different types of insects visit vernal pool flowers, some have evolved to depend on only one or a few types of flowers. See page 13 for more information on the specialist bees that feed their offspring with the pollen of vernal pool flowers.

Goldfields and popcorn-flowers prefer the wetter inner margins.

Another unusual survival adaptation of vernal pool plants is their strategy for seed dispersal. Most don't even try to disperse their seeds. Having evolved to live in a flooded area for most of their life, and requiring a drying down phase to stimulate flowering and seed production—why would they want to cast their seeds into unsuitable habitat? A number of vernal pool species actually plant their seeds at the base of their parent plant. This ensures that the seeds are in the best possible location to germinate, grow and reproduce next year.

Navarretias like wet areas where the hardpan is very close to the surface.

Being an annual plant with dedicated pollinators and setting seed quickly is a good way to deal with the short spring and long drought phases of this habitat. Vernal pool plants have also had to develop other adaptations to deal with the aquatic phase. Most plants would drown if flooded for long periods. Vernal pool plants deal with this in several unique ways. Some pipe air to their roots through long, hollow stems or leaves. Others absorb atmospheric gasses (air) directly from the water.

California Native Plant Society

Coyote thistle during the aquatic phase.

Coyote thistle during the early flowering phase.

Coyote thistle during the early drought phase.

Coyote thistle is one of the vernal pool endemic plants that has evolved a unique way to pipe air to its roots. During the aquatic phase, the plant produces hollow, cylindrical leaves that stick up out of the water. Air gets to the plant's roots through this tube. Later, as the pools dry, these leaves become solid, leafier and spiny. The photos above show the amazing physical changes that coyote thistles go through each year.

Other vernal pool plants bring air to their roots by producing floating leaves. The leaves can absorb enough air for the entire plant. This adaptation also has the advantage of shading out other plants, thereby reducing competition. Vernal pool buttercups (page 24), meadow foxtail (page 35), and vernal pool hairgrass (page 34) all employ this strategy for surviving the aquatic phase.

Many vernal pool plants spend the aquatic phase entirely under water. They survive by absorbing dissolved gasses directly from the water. But because warm water has less dissolved gasses than cold water, they absorb air from the cooler water at night. Several groups of plants, including many desert species, absorb air at night instead of during the day, but only vernal pool plants do it under water.

Because vernal pool plants are native to their environment, they have had tens of thousands of years to adapt to the extreme conditions of living in a vernal pool. Most non-native species cannot survive in a vernal pool.

Mather Field vernal pool at the peak of the flowering phase.
Photo by Eva Butler.

Drought Phase

During the hot, dry summer months, vernal pools lie brown and barren. The drought phase begins as the last of the water evaporates and the soils begin to dry out. The aquatic organisms have been gone for a month or more, but have deposited their cysts to ensure the next generation. By now the grasslands are brown and dormant until the rains return in the fall. Most of the vernal pool plants have also set seed and have withered and died. The drought phase can last for 6-8 months.

Dormant vernal pool fairy shrimp cysts and gravel.
Photo by Mark Loeb.

Coyote thistle waits until the heat of summer to bloom and produce seed.

The drought phase is absolutely necessary for the plants and animals that call vernal pools their home. Without the drought phase, the cysts and seeds could not produce a new generation next year. They need to bake under the summer sun before they can be triggered into hatching or germinating when the rains return in the fall and winter.

That is one reason why it is important to prevent summer garden water runoff from entering the vernal pool landscape. Another reason is the introduction of pesticides that would kill the vernal pool animals and plants.

But even in the drought phase the vernal pool landscape is far from dead. Some of the vernal pool plants wait until the heat of summer to bloom and set seed. Insects, birds and animals continue to visit the vernal pools. They come to feed on the cysts and seeds left behind. When they do, other critters come to feed upon them. Thus, vernal pools form a large and very complex food chain critical to the survival of many species.

A vernal pool in the drought phase. For the uninformed, it can be difficult to see where the grassland ends and the pool begins.
Photo by David Rosen.

Native Specialist Pollinators

Vernal pools are noted for their multi-colored rings and ribbons of native flowers. Each species occupies a different topographic position and micro-habitat within the pool. And each produces a dense and abundant display of flowers which all bloom at the same time.

Abundant display of flowers that bloom in a vernal pool.
Photo by Mike Eaton.

Besides delighting the eye of human visitors, there is an important ecological reason for the flowers of a given species to bloom in mass synchrony. Many of the showiest vernal pool flowers (yellow carpet, meadowfoam, goldfields, and downingia) are pollinated by native specialist bees in the family Andrenidae. These solitary, ground-nesting bees use the pollen of specific flowers to feed their young. And, during the course of collecting pollen to provision their nests, they perform the vital function of cross-pollinating the vernal pool flowers.

A female solitary, pollen specialist bee (Andrena [Hesperandrena] baeriae) collecting pollen from goldfields (Lasthenia sp.).
For more information on specialist pollinators visit www.vernalpools.org/Thorp.
This and all subsequent native pollinator photos by Dennis Briggs and courtesy of Robbin W. Thorp.

Each of the four plant groups listed above has one or more native specialist bee that collects pollen only from them. Female bees that collect pollen from one or a few closely related flowers are called oligolectic (from *oligo* = few, *legene* = to gather). They require pollen from the flowers to provide protein for the development of their offspring. The life cycle of these bees is closely synchronized with that of their pollen host flowers.

While generalist and non-native bees, such as the honey bee, and other insects also visit most of these flowers and may potentially pollinate them, research shows that at least some of these flowers may require their specialist pollinators for successful reproduction and seed set.

Vernal Pools of Mather Field

A female specialist bee, *Panurginus occidentalis*, collecting pollen from white meadowfoam.

A female specialist bee, *Andrena blennospermatis*, collecting pollen from yellow carpet.

A female specialist bee, *Panurginus* "new species", collecting pollen from horned downingia.

The Lifecycle of Native Specialist Bees

This open tumulus indicates that the female bee is out foraging for pollen and/or nectar.

A completed brood cell showing its shiny, water-proof lining. The female bee uses body secretions to create this water-proofing.

Female bees in the family Andrenidae, which specialize on pollen of vernal pool flowers, are on the wing only in early spring when their host plants are in flower. The life cycle of the bee is closely tuned to that of its host plant's bloom period. The bees emerge at or just before their host flowers start to bloom. Male bees emerge shortly before the females. Mating occurs as soon as females emerge. Females initiate construction of their brood nests immediately after mating.

The female bees construct their nests in the soil of the upland areas surrounding vernal pools. The presence of such bee nests is revealed by ant mound-like clumps of excavated soil (tumuli) at the surface of the soil. A closed tumulus indicates the female is in her burrow constructing it. An open tumulus indicates the female bee is afield foraging for pollen and/or nectar as provisions for her offspring.

The basic nest architecture consists of a vertical shaft penetrating the soil for a few inches before becoming a lateral tunnel ending in a single brood chamber. A newly constructed brood chamber has a

Early stages of provisioning the brood chamber.

A newly hatched larva of the specialist bee on its food ball, a combination of pollen and nectar from the specific plant it requires for nutrition.

Fully developed larva that will eventually transform into a bee. That bee will remain underground until its host flowers bloom again.

polished look because of its water-proof lining. This waxy lining is secreted by the female and painted over the inner surface of the brood cell.

When brood chamber construction is complete, the female bee forages for pollen on her preferred host flowers. She grooms pollen from her body and packs it into specialized brushes of hair on her hind legs for transport back to her nest. As the dry pollen food provisions accumulate in the brood cell, the female adds nectar, moistening the mass to a dough-like consistency. When the pollen ball is complete, she lays an egg on top. She then constructs a plug closing off the entrance to the chamber with spirally-arranged soil particles. After closing off the brood chamber the mother bee has no further contact with her offspring.

A newly hatched larva begins feeding on the provisions. After consuming all of the pollen ball, the larva transforms into an adult. The adult sits in the brood chamber until the following spring when it emerges to continue its life cycle in association with the flowering of its pollen host plant.

Why Protect Uplands?

Current regulatory laws that help to protect vernal pools are based entirely on the wetland areas. There are no laws that help to protect the grassland adjacent to the vernal pools. And yet, the previous discussion on the life cycle of the pollinators that depend upon and provide vital services to vernal pool plants shows that preservation of adjacent uplands is not only important, but vital, to the overall health of this ecosystem. Without the native specialist bees to pollinate them, many vernal pool plants will perish.

California Annual Grasslands

Most Central Valley vernal pools occur within a matrix of annual grassland. The grasslands occupy the uplands surrounding the vernal pools. While often dominated by non-native European annual grasses, these grasslands are the last remaining home for many native plants that were once much more common.

When John Muir entered the Central Valley of California in 1868, he wrote:

"When I first saw this central garden... it seemed all one sheet of plant gold, hazy and vanishing in the distance... At length I waded out into the midst of it. All the ground was covered... Sauntering in any direction, hundreds of these happy sun-plants brushed against my feet at every step, and closed over them as if I were wading in liquid gold."

A glimpse of what John Muir may have been describing in 1868 when he first visited the Central Valley.

So what happened to the abundant fields of wildflowers so poetically described by Muir during his first trek across California? The answer is both simple and complex. The simple answer is that non-native plants moved in and virtually displaced the native species. The more complex answer revolves around a series of human history events that forever changed the face of California and its Central Valley.

The human saga that led to the changes in our plants (and animals) begins in the mid-1500s when trading ships sailed up and down the California coast. Though they didn't come ashore due to the rocky coast, they did throw their garbage overboard. The first wave of non-native plants entered California by drifting ashore. Most notably, filaree (page 26) began its colonization of California at that time. It was widespread by the time the first settlers arrived.

Then in the late 1700s, Europeans began to colonize California from Mexico. They brought their favorite edible, medicinal and ornamental plants. Many more seeds were inadvertently introduced from the fur and droppings of their domestic animals. But this early colonization was rather limited and did not impact vast acreages.

During the next century, many people immigrated to California from both the east and the south. They too brought along their favorite non-native plants and domestic animals and plowed land to grow their crops. But they were also relatively few in number and did not significantly alter the face of California.

Then along comes 1849! During the gold rush, hundreds of thousands of miners moved into California. Along with them came the entrepreneurs who made their money from feeding, housing and entertaining the miners. During the gold rush boom, California saw its most drastic changes in the environment. If land was fertile enough to plow and plant wheat, it became a wheat field. If it wasn't, then massive herds of grazing animals were brought in to feed the hungry miners. Eventually, the native plants were suppressed or replaced by this onslaught of over-utilization.

When John Muir visited the Central Valley in 1868, the displacement of the native vegetation was only just beginning. Since then, millions of people have moved to California and vast acreages have been converted to intensive agriculture or other uses. The lands remaining for native plants continue to shrink, while threats from invasive non-native plants continue to grow.

Annuals such as this tidy-tip find their only remaining home in the California annual grasslands. Based on historical photos, tidy-tips were once much more common in the Central Valley.

Despite the radical changes in the plant composition of California annual grasslands, they still remain the last refuge for many native species. The grasslands that form the matrix around Central Valley vernal pools are particulary important for conserving these native wildflowers and their important pollinators. These species cannot live or prosper in agricultural fields or urban lots.

In order to enjoy the native plants in the annual grasslands, it is important to time your visit carefully. By late spring or early summer, all of the delicate native annuals have set seed and perished, and the only plants you will observe are the non-natives. If you visit during the early spring, you may be delighted by the abundance of native wildflowers in grasslands.

Bulb-producing natives such as this brodiaea are also very common in California annual grasslands.

Grazing: Good or Bad?

This is a conundrum that has been debated in both environmental and land management circles for the past decade or more. Cows and sheep are not native to the California grasslands. Therefore many environmentalists arrived at the seemingly logical conclusion that grazing is bad for the vernal pool environment and its native plants. Land managers tended to focus on economic impacts and for them, grazing was a necessary component of the landscape. For years, there was a general agreement to disagree.

Recently published scientific studies show that removal of grazing from a vernal pool area had a significant detrimental impact on both vernal pools and their surrounding grasslands. Weeds and other non-native plants increased and native plants decreased. Even the aquatic organisms seemed to suffer a decline in abundance. The studies show that grazing animals are necessary to control the accumulation of thatch that originates from the non-native annual grasses, and which would eventually choke out many of the native species.

Ungrazed (foreground) and grazed grasslands.
Photo by Stuart Weiss.

Yet Mather Field has not been grazed for at least 70 years and appears to have healthy vernal pools and lots of pretty native wildflowers in the grassland. To a knowledgeable observer, there is also an abundance of weedy, non-native species in both the pools and grassland. One of many observations about Mather Field versus nearby grazed lands is that there are native plants present on Mather Field that are absent or rare on the grazed lands. Another observation is that some native plants abundant on adjacent grazed lands are rarely seen or even absent at Mather Field. If grazing is reintroduced at Mather Field, will we gain abundance of some species while losing others, or will we just lose species? These big questions require detailed long-term scientific study before any changes in land management are made.

For more information about the grazing study in vernal pool grasslands of Sacramento County, see www.vernalpools.org/Marty.

Conservation versus Mitigation

The California Native Plant Society is dedicated to the conservation of our native flora in its natural habitat. Vernal pools are a unique natural habitat and are home to hundreds of native species that can live nowhere else. More than 90% of the vernal pools that originally occurred in California have already been destroyed. It would seem only logical to protect the vernal pools that remain. Some may even believe they are already protected because of the endangered species that live in them. But vernal pools continue to be destroyed at an escalating rate throughout California, especially the Central Valley.

Two important resource-protection laws govern the activities that take place in and around vernal pools: the federal Clean Water Act (CWA) and the federal Endangered Species Act (ESA). The CWA regulates the discharge of fill material into our wetlands and waters. Because vernal pools are wetlands, destroying them is subject to that federal law. The ESA cover a number of threatened and endangered species that live in vernal pools. But, neither of these two laws actually prevent destruction of vernal pools—they only regulate it.

Under both laws, projects that will destroy vernal pools and kill endangered species can be approved—provided that the impacts are *mitigated*. Under the CWA, mitigation generally takes the form of building replacement vernal pool wetlands. Endangered species can be killed and their habitat destroyed, as long as a project is mitigated and doesn't clearly cause extinction. ESA mitigation usually involves the creation of so-called replacement habitat plus the added benefit of preserving some natural habitat elsewhere.

Vernal pools have been around for millennia. The plants and animals that depend upon them rely upon more than just a man-made rain puddle that dries down in the summer. The soil and water chemistries of natural vernal pools are unique and influence the species that occupy them. Many of the vernal pool endemic plants depend upon plant-specific insect pollinators that fly only short distances. The laws only require a few short years of very minimal monitoring before the created pools can be declared successful. Many created pools that were once declared successful mitigation have declined following the required monitoring period.

Does vernal pool mitigation really replace a natural ecosystem that took many thousands of years to evolve and thrive, or is it just producing sad imitations destined to perish because they lack all of the species and conditions that make a vernal pool ecosystem function?

To find out more about how you can help to preserve vernal pools, visit: www.vernalpools.org or www.sacvalleycnps.org.

P
L
A
N
T
S

Jointed Wild Radish
Raphanus raphanistrum

APR-JUN
1-4 FEET
INTRODUCED

Occurs primarily in disturbed grasslands. Flowers are 1" and white to pale yellow. Seed pods have a radish-like flavor when young.

Valley Tassels
Castilleja attenuata

MAR-APR
6-12 INCHES
NATIVE

This grassland species is also known as white-tipped owl's-clover. The flowers are long tubes with three inflated sacks near the top which have a series of pink, yellow and black spots that resemble tiny faces.

Mouse-ear Chickweed
Cerastium glomeratum

MAR-MAY
1-12 INCHES
INTRODUCED

Common weed in many habitats of California. At Mather Field it prefers slightly mesic areas such as the edges of vernal pools or along the intermittent creeks.

White Hyacinth
Triteleia hyacinthina

APR-MAY
12-18 INCHES
NATIVE

White hyacinth is a bulb-producing perennial grassland plant. Early in the season the plants produce one or a few grass-like leaves. By the time the flowers are ready to bloom the leaves have dried up.

Field Popcorn Flower
Plagiobothrys fulvus

MAR-MAY
1-3 FEET
NATIVE

The flowers are arranged in a coil or spiral, with the outermost flowers blooming first. As the spiral uncoils, the flowers bloom sequentially up the stalk. The hairs on this plant can be irritating to the skin.

Vernal Pool Popcorn Flower
APR-JUN
4-8 INCHES
Plagiobothrys stipitatus var. *micranthus*   NATIVE

The flowers shown are only ¼ inch across. This small, delicate plant is a California vernal pool endemic. It can be quite common in vernal pools at Mather Field.

White Navarretia
APR-MAY
1-4 INCHES
Navarretia leucocephala   NATIVE

This vernal pool endemic often blankets the bottom of pools. Its flowers are a favorite nectar source for a number of small blue or copper butterflies.

White Meadowfoam
MAR-MAY
6-12 INCHES
Limnanthes alba   NATIVE

Abundant in wet grassland. It is common around vernal pools, but also occurs on slopes that are wet in the early spring. Meadowfoam is pollinated by native solitary bees (see page 13).

Bractless Hedge-hyssop
MAR-MAY
1-6 INCHES
Gratiola ebracteata   NATIVE

Occurs in wet, muddy places throughout most of the Pacific states. At Mather Field, this species can be common in the deeper vernal pools.

Bindweed
MAR-OCT
VINE
Convolvulus arvensis   INVASIVE

Bindweed plants produce extensive and very deep (30 feet) root systems. It has been a serious weed in California for nearly a century. Fortunately the above-ground parts die back every year and do not smother other plants.

P
L
A
N
T
S

P
L
A
N
T
S

Caraway-leaved Lomatium

FEB-MAR
6-12 INCHES
NATIVE

Lomatium caruifolium

Occurs in grasslands. Native Americans used the dried roots to make a flour from which a type of biscuit was made. Early settlers used the foliage as an herb to spice stews, soups, and preserved meats.

Frying Pan Poppy

FEB-MAY
4-12 INCHES
NATIVE

Eschscholzia lobbii

Common in the grasslands. Native Americans and early Spanish-Californians used a poultice made from the leaves and roots to make their hair shiny.

Fiddleneck

MAR-JUN
1-4 FEET
INTRODUCED

Amsinckia menziesii var. *intermedia*

Occurs primarily in grassland where the soils have been disturbed. Flowers occur in a coil or spiral, with the outermost blooming first. Hairs can be irritating to the skin.

Butter & Eggs

FEB-APR
4-6 INCHES
NATIVE

Triphysaria eriantha

Also known as Johnny-tuck or common owl's-clover, this species occurs in moist grasslands. This plant is a hemiparasite and derives some of its nutrition from parasitizing the roots of other plants.

Field Owl's Clover

APR-JUN
4-8 INCHES
NATIVE

Castilleja campestris

Endemic to California vernal pools. Common at Mather Field. Distinguishable from the related butter & eggs by the green, linear leaves. This plant is not parasitic.

Yellow Carpet

FEB-MAR
2-5 INCHES
NATIVE

Blennosperma nanum

Occurs in moist grassland and vernal pools. Not very common at Mather Field because the accumulation of dead grass prevents it from germinating. Pollinated by native solitary bees (see page 13).

Fremont's Tidy-tips

MAR-APR
6-10 INCHES
NATIVE

Layia fremontii

Common in moist grassland. The white circle with yellow center is like a bull's-eye or target to guide the pollinating insects to the nectar in the center of the flower.

Vernal Pool Goldfields

MAR-MAY
4-6 INCHES
NATIVE

Lasthenia fremontii

Endemic to California vernal pools and quite common in most vernal pools. Pollinated by native solitary bees in the Andrenidae family (see page 13).

Hawkbit

MAR-JUL
8-14 INCHES
INTRODUCED

Leontodon taraxacoides

Occurs in vernal pools and grasslands. This is one of the few non-native species that has been able to invade vernal pools. Its native habitat in Europe is also seasonal wetlands.

Narrow-leaved Mule's Ear

APR-JUN
1-2 FEET
NATIVE

Wyethia angustifolia

This large (4") flowered, perennial plant occurs in grasslands. Common at Mather Field because of the lack of grazing. But the lack of grazing has eliminated other native plants that occur in nearby rangelands.

P
L
A
N
T
S

Vernal Pool Buttercup

MAR-MAY
4-10 INCHES
NATIVE

Ranunculus bonariensis var. *trisepalus*

Endemic to California vernal pools. When aquatic, the plant has floating leaves with very long stems. Later, the leaves have shorter stems and the plant blooms. Yellow petals are tiny, but the fruit resembles a raspberry.

Rayless Goldfields

APR-JUN
3-6 INCHES
NATIVE

Lasthenia glaberrima

Occurs in vernal pools and other seasonally wet places. While the common name may imply that it has no rayflowers, close inspection with a handlens will reveal that it does have rayflowers, but that they are very small.

Hop Clover

MAR-APR
4-10 INCHES
INTRODUCED

Trifolium dubium

Many non-native clovers were introduced during agricultural enhancement projects in the 1930s to improve forage. Many ranchers took advantage of these programs. Hop clover was probably introduced at that time.

Seep Spring Monkeyflower

MAR-AUG
6-24 INCHES
NATIVE

Mimulus guttatus

Occurs along tributaries to Morrison Creek and on the margins of some vernal pools. The red dots at the throat of the flower are a guide to pollinators.

Gum Plant

MAY-JUL
1-2 FEET
NATIVE

Grindelia camporum

While this is a native species, it tends to prefer disturbed areas. All parts of the plant are very sticky (or shiny) in appearance. Generally blooms well after the annual grasses have dried.

Photo by Sacramento Splash.

Spring Madia
APR-MAY
1-3 FEET
NATIVE

Madia elegans ssp. *vernalis*

Can be quite common in the grassland. Plants are very aromatic and have sticky yellow or black gland-tipped hairs.

P
L
A
N
T
S

Fitch's Spikeweed
MAY-JUL
1-2 FEET
NATIVE

Hemizonia fitchii

Fitch's spikeweed has hypodermic-like needles on the tips of the upper leaves. The hairs are gland-tipped and give off a strong aroma. Similar species are named 'tarweeds' because of their stickiness.

Yellow Starthistle
MAY-OCT
1-4 FEET
INVASIVE

Centaurea solstitialis

Yellow starthistle is one of the worst weeds in California. Its deep taproot allows it to out-compete other species for summer soil moisture. Seeds can remain viable for at least three years.

Photo by Jennifer Hogan.

Gold Nuggets
MAY-JUN
8-14 INCHES
NATIVE

Calochortus luteus

This bulb plant blooms late in the season when the grasslands are nearly dry. Flowers are beetle pollinated and you may see several species visiting the flowers. Another common name for this plant is yellow mariposa lily.

Klamath Weed
APR-JUN
1-3 FEET
INVASIVE

Hypericum perforatum

Originally from Europe, this weed nearly took over the Pacific northwest. It is currently under control in that area by a bioagent (an introduced beetle); but that beetle cannot survive the dry summer heat of the Central Valley.

Filaree

Erodium botrys

FEB-MAY
1-5 INCHES
INTRODUCED

One of the earliest grassland invaders of California. Seeds coil when it is hot and dry, and uncoil during the cooler evening temperatures. This allows them to "locomote" across the ground and find new habitat.

Cut-leaf Filaree

Erodium cicutarium

FEB-MAY
1-6 INCHES
INTRODUCED

Widespread weed of disturbed areas. Cut-leaf filaree is especially common in areas with highly compacted soils, such as road edges.

Wild Radish

Raphanus sativus

FEB-JUN
1-4 FEET
INTRODUCED

Flowers generally pale pink to lavender. The seed pods have a distinctive radish-like flavor, especially when young. Produces mustard oils that were used to make a toxic gas used during World War I.

Red Maids

Calandrinia ciliata

FEB-APR
3-12 INCHES
NATIVE

While native, they often occur in disturbed areas. Look for them on old gopher mounds. Also known as poor man's weather vane, they only open when the sun is shining.

Vernal Pool Monkeyflower

Mimulus tricolor

MAR-MAY
2-4 INCHES
NATIVE

Endemic to California vernal pools. The genus name is from the word for mimic, hence the common name of monkeyflower. This plant can be particularly abundant on old gopher mounds in the vernal pools.

PLANTS

Rose Clover

APR-JUN
1-2 FEET
INTRODUCED

Trifolium hirtum

Rose clover can be invasive in some areas of California. It readily colonizes disturbed areas and chokes out native plants. At Mather Field, it is most commonly observed along the roads and in other disturbed places.

Dwarf Sack Clover

MAR-MAY
4-10 INCHES
NATIVE

Trifolium depauperatum

Common in moist grasslands. When in seed, the individual flowers inflate (as shown) and resemble small sacks. Clovers are highly nutritious to animals that occupy the grassland ecosystem.

White-Tipped Clover

MAR-MAY
4-10 INCHES
NATIVE

Trifolium variegatum

One of the loveliest of the native clovers. This sweet-smelling species rings many of the vernal pools at Mather Field. Besides being lovely and fragrant, the honey produced from these flowers is one of the best tasting of all.

Vernal Pool Checkerbloom

MAR-MAY
6-18 INCHES
NATIVE

Sidalcea calycosa

This species blooms along with white-tipped clover on the edges of the vernal pools. Observe the many small black beetles commonly found in the center of the flower. These are the pollinators of this plant.

Alkali Checkerbloom

APR-MAY
6-18 INCHES
NATIVE

Sidalcea hirsuta

Occurs in the grasslands just above the vernal pools and on damp slopes. It is much darker pink than the related vernal pool checkerbloom.

P
L
A
N
T
S

P
L
A
N
T
S

Hairy Pea

Lathyrus hirsutus

APR-MAY
6-12 INCHES
INTRODUCED

This tiny pea is distinguished by two leaflets below the coiling tendril. It uses the tendril to 'climb' other plants. While hairy pea is non-native, its small stature means that it generally cannot out-compete native species.

Spanish Lotus

Lotus purshianus

MAY-OCT
4-18 INCHES
NATIVE

Foliage is quite noticeable during most of the spring throughout the grasslands. Late in the season, tiny pale pink pea blossoms appear. The seeds are large and quite nutritious. They are eaten by birds and burrowing mammals.

June Centaury

Centaurium muehlenbergii

MAY-JUL
3-18 INCHES
NATIVE

June centaury occurs in a variety of wetland habitats. In vernal pools, it is usually quite small and single-flowered. In areas that are wet in the summer, the plants can be robust and have a large, open cluster of flowers.

Cut-leaf Geranium

Geranium dissectum

MAR-MAY
6-18 INCHES
INTRODUCED

Prefers open, moist, disturbed locations. Cut-leaf geranium occurs most abundantly along the intermittent stream channels and around adjacent vernal pools.

Bocconi's Sand-spurrey

Spergularia bocconii

APR-JUN
2-10 INCHES
INTRODUCED

The pink, five-petaled flowers are only ¼ inch across. Bocconi's sand-spurrey occurs in disturbed areas and along road sides. It prefers areas with little to no competition from other plants.

Italian Thistle

APR-JUN
1-4 FEET
INTRODUCED

Carduus pycnocephalus

Can be highly invasive in grasslands, especially in disturbed areas. In our area, Italian thistle is generally a biennial. The overwintering rosettes shade out other plants.

Milk Thistle

APR-JUL
2-5 FEET
INTRODUCED

Silybum marianum

Can be highly invasive in disturbed areas. At Mather Field there are currently only occasional small patches. This could change rapidly with disturbances caused by urban infrastructure development.

Sheep Sorrel

MAR-APR
1-2 FEET
INTRODUCED

Rumex acetosella

During the early spring, this plant makes its presence noticeable by providing pink patches that appear to be a light mist over the grassland. While non-native, this species is not invasive at Mather Field.

Scarlett Pimpernel

ALL YEAR
2-6 INCHES
INTRODUCED

Anagallis arvensis

This is a common weed of lawns and disturbed areas. It has also found its way into the California grassland ecosystem. While not considered particularly invasive, it can displace native species on the margins of vernal pools.

Purple Sanicle

MAR-MAY
1-3 FEET
NATIVE

Sanicula bipinnatifida

Occurs in grasslands. Another common name is purple snakeroot. This is because of a Native American medicinal use in which a poultice of the carrot-like root was used to treat snakebites.

P
L
A
N
T
S

P
L
A
N
T
S

Bluedicks

MAR-MAY
8-16 INCHES
NATIVE

Dichelostemma capitatum

This plant is a perennial bulb that occurs in grasslands. The bulbs are famous for being a major food item for Native Americans as well as gophers. Most plants only produce flowers every few years.

Wild Hyacinth

APR-MAY
12-18 INCHES
NATIVE

Dichelostemma multiflorum

As with many of the perennial, bulb-forming grassland plants, the bulbs are highly nutritious and flavorful. They are eaten by burrowing rodents and were harvested by Native Americans.

Wally Baskets

MAR-APR
1-2 FEET
NATIVE

Triteleia laxa

Also called Ithuriel's spear, this is very common flower of California grasslands. The flowers are generally pale blue at Mather Field, but can be white to purplish-blue elsewhere. The pollen of this plant is blue.

Crown Brodiaea

MAR-APR
12-18 INCHES
NATIVE

Brodiaea coronaria

This perennial bulb forming plant can be common in the grasslands. The underground bulbs are nutty flavored and nutritious. They are consumed by Botta's pocket gophers and were harvested by Native Americans.

Elegant Brodiaea

MAY-JUN
12-18 INCHES
NATIVE

Brodiaea elegans

This bulb-forming plant generally blooms after the grasses have set seed. The tall purple flowers make a striking contrast with the brown grasses. Elegant brodiaea is pollinated by native beetles.

Vernal Pool Brodiaea

APR-JUN
3-6 INCHES
NATIVE

Brodiaea minor

Blooms mid-season and is generally found in vernal pools. It can be distinguished from the other Brodiaeas by its short stature and it has a distinct constriction above the ovary. Its bulbs are also highly nutritious.

Horned Downingia

APR-MAY
3-5 INCHES
NATIVE

Downingia bicornuta var. *picta*

Endemic to California vernal pools. Can be distinguished from related species by the two horns at the throat of the flower. Downingias are pollinated by native solitary bees (see page 13).

Toothed Downingia

APR-MAY
2-4 INCHES
NATIVE

Downingia cuspidata

Endemic to California vernal pools. It is distinguished from other related species at Mather Field by its upright upper petals and by the lack of any dark markings in its throat.

P L A N T S

Folded Downingia

APR-MAY
2-4 INCHES
NATIVE

Downingia ornatissima

Endemic to California vernal pools. It can be distinguished from related species by the upper petals, which curl to the sides, and by the slight horn that grows outward from between the upper petals.

Douglas's Beardstyle

APR-JUL
4-8 INCHES
NATIVE

Pogogyne douglasii

Endemic to vernal pools on the eastern side of the Central Valley. Occurs in only a few vernal pools at Mather Field, but when it does it can be the dominant species. The foliage smells like mint.

Sacramento Beardstyle

Pogogyne zizyphoroides

MAR-JUN
1-5 INCHES
NATIVE

Endemic to Sacramento Valley vernal pools. Lavender flowers are generally less than 3 mm across. Can occur in both pools and adjacent moist grasslands. The plants have a strong minty smell, with chocolate overtones.

Miniature Lupine

Lupinus bicolor

MAR-MAY
4-12 INCHES
NATIVE

The smallest-flowered lupine in California. A common and sometimes abundant component of the grasslands. This plant is noticeable for its palmate (palm-shaped) leaves and later for the large pea pods which hold the seeds.

Winter Vetch

Vicia villosa

MAR-JUL
1-3 FEET
INTRODUCED

Originally introduced to augment the nutritional value of grazing lands. Vetches fix atmospheric nitrogen and store it in their roots. This enriches the soil which, in turn, can make it more hospitable to weedy species.

Vinegar Weed

Trichostema lanceolatum

JUL-OCT
1-3 FEET
NATIVE

Blooms after most of the grassland and vernal pool plants have withered and dried. Foliage is strongly scented and smells like vinegar and camphor. Also known as camphor weed.

What's in a name?

People use names and other descriptive terms to communicate— house, car, green, soft, etc. When trying to talk about specific plants and animals, this becomes complicated due to regional variations in the common name applied to an organism. When talking about a specific plant or animal, scientists and knowledgable laymen generally prefer to use its scientific, or 'official', name to avoid any confusion.

Shining Peppergrass

FEB-APR
2-6 INCHES
NATIVE

Lepidium nitidum

This plant has tiny white flowers that are not readily noticeable. Its most striking feature are its lens-shaped seed pods. Because of its spicy mustard flavor, it was used as an herb by early settlers.

Spokepod

FEB-APR
4-18 INCHES
NATIVE

Thysanocarpus radians

Can be abundant in the grasslands. Tiny white flowers give rise to unique wheel-shaped seed pods. These plants have a bitter flavor caused by mustard oils, to help protect them from some herbivores.

Wall Bedstraw

APR-MAY
3-6 INCHES
INTRODUCED

Galium parisiense

The tiny pink flowers are not as noticeable as the whorls of leaves along the angular stems. This plant is very common in the grasslands at Mather Field. It tends to prefer growing on old gopher mounds.

Coyote Thistle

MAY-JUL
6-24 INCHES
NATIVE

Eryngium castrense

The photo shown is typical of this plant in the early spring. In summer it will bloom with multiple heads of tiny purple flowers. This is one of the plants that has special adaptations (see page 11) to live in vernal pools.

Soap Root

MAY-JUN
3-4 FEET
NATIVE

Chlorogalum pomeridianum

Soap root has a distinct rosette of wavy-margined leaves. Late in the season it will put up a tall, branched stock with small white flowers that bloom at night. Native Americans used the root of this plant to stun fish.

P
L
A
N
T
S

Woolly Marbles

APR-MAY
1-4 INCHES
NATIVE

Psilocarphus brevissimus

This vernal pool endemic is shown during the height of its blooming period. The minute flowers are enclosed in tiny, hairy sacks in the center of the flowerhead. Later in the season, the plant will resemble a small woolly marble.

Vernal Pool Dodder

JUN-AUG
STRINGY
NATIVE

Cuscuta howelliana

This vernal pool endemic plant is a parasite. It derives all of its nutrition by stealing it from other plants. It even steals pollinators; the tiny orange flowers bloom inside the flower heads of other vernal pool plants such as navarretia.

Little Quaking Grass

MAR-JUL
4-12 INCHES
INTRODUCED

Briza minor

The flower clusters resemble rattlesnake tails when examined with a handlens. While this grass is not native to California grasslands, it does not out-compete native species.

Silver Hairgrass

MAR-JUN
4-8 INCHES
INTRODUCED

Aira caryophyllea

While this grass is not native to California grasslands, its small stature makes it a "naturalized" member of the vernal pool grassland community and does not out-compete native species.

Vernal Pool Hairgrass

MAR-JUN
1-2 FEET
NATIVE

Deschampsia danthonioides

This delicate, annual grass is endemic to vernal pools. It most often occurs in vernal pools dominated by vernal pool goldfields (see page 23) where it forms a purplish-red 'mist' over the sea of golden flowers.

P
L
A
N
T
S

Meadow Foxtail

Alopecurus saccatus

APR-JUL
4-10 INCHES
NATIVE

Native, annual grass endemic to vernal pools. During the winter, the floating leaves shade the soil, and prevent other species from germinating. Notice the white pollen which is carried by the wind from plant to plant.

Soft Chess Brome

Bromus hordeaceus

APR-JUL
6-24 INCHES
INTRODUCED

This European grass is one of the most common in California grasslands. While non-native, it is not aggressively weedy. California voles and many other native grassland animals consume its seeds.

Wild Oats

Avena fatua

APR-JUN
2-4 FEET
INTRODUCED

A native of Europe, wild oats is common in grasslands throughout the United States and Canada. At Mather Field, this grass generally occurs only in areas with deeper soils.

Italian Ryegrass

Lolium multiflorum

APR-MAY
1-3 FEET
INTRODUCED

A native of Europe, this grass occupies moist grasslands. The plant contains a substance that inhibits the germination of many other plants. Therefore, it is often found in dense patches with few other plants present.

Pale Spikerush

Eleocharis macrostachya

APR-JUN
1-2 FEET
NATIVE

One of the only perennial species that occupies vernal pools. When aquatic, it is hollow to transport gasses to the roots. When terrestrial, the stems fill with pith to give the plants more structural stability.

P
L
A
N
T
S

35

Mediterranean Barley

APR-JUN
4-10 INCHES
INTRODUCED

Hordeum marinum

This is one of the few Mediterranean grasses that can occupy vernal pools. It generally occurs on the margins of the pools where water ponds for the shortest period of time.

Foxtail Barley

APR-JUN
1-2 FEET
INTRODUCED

Hordeum murinum

This grass prefers deeper soils and disturbed areas. At Mather Field it is common along roadsides. The seed-head has backward facing hairs that allow it to lodge in the ears of dogs and other domestic animals.

Ripgut Brome

APR-JUN
1-3 FEET
INTRODUCED

Bromus diandrus

A very coarse, non-native grass that prefers deeper soils and disturbed areas. As the common name implies, this species is avoided by grazers, both native and domestic, because it causes harm to their stomachs.

Barbed Goatgrass

MAY-JUL
1-2 FEET
INVASIVE

Aegilops triuncialis

Barbed Goatgrass has been invading California grasslands for the last decade or so. It appears to be very adaptable and can occupy extreme habitats. It is generally unpalatable to livestock and cannot be controlled by grazing.

Medusahead

APR-JUN
6-14 INCHES
INVASIVE

Taeniatherium caput-medusae

One of the worst rangeland weeds of California. This grass contains a large amount of silica (glass). It is not palatable to most grazing animals and creates a dense thatch that prevents germination of native plants.

P
L
A
N
T
S

Coyote Bush

Baccharis pilularis

JUL-AUG
SHRUB
NATIVE

Common shrub on some of the grassland terraces east of Eagles Nest Road. Each shrub is either male or female. Male plants produce pale yellow flowers. Female plants produce white flowers.

Blue Oak

Quercus douglasii

APR-MAY
TREE
NATIVE

Blue oaks are deciduous trees that occur in dry grasslands, especially in the foothills. They have distinctive blue-green, slightly-lobed leaves. The trunk has gray bark. The acorns mature in a single year and are oval shaped.

Valley Oak

Quercus lobata

MAR-APR
TREE
NATIVE

The valley oak is a deciduous tree that occurs primarily on the deeper valley soils. It has dark gray-green, deeply-lobed leaves. The bark has a checkered pattern. Acorns mature in one year and are long and skinny.

Interior Live Oak

Quercus wislizenii

MAR-APR
TREE
NATIVE

The interior live oak is an evergreen tree, often with multiple trunks. The leaves are shiny green and have spines along their slightly-lobed margins. The acorns need two years to mature and are oval.

Fremont's Cottonwood

Populus fremontii

MAR-APR
TREE
NATIVE

Cottonwoods generally occur near streams. This deciduous tree has smooth bark that becomes furrowed with age. The heart-shaped leaves have flattened stems that cause the leaves to flutter in the slightest breeze.

P
L
A
N
T
S

What is a rare plant?

Plants can be rare, threatened or endangered for a variety of reasons. Many plants have evolved to live in a certain place, or only in areas that have specific micro-habitat conditions. Rare plants that occupy vernal pools are often also restricted to specific geographic areas. Habitat loss to urbanization and more intensive agricultural uses are the primary threats to the rare plants that live in vernal pools.

Ahart's Dwarf Rush

MAR-APR
1-3 INCHES
RARE

Juncus leiospermus var. *ahartii*

Considered rare and endangered throughout its range by the California Native Plant Society.

This dimuntive rush is known from only a dozen or so locations, all within California. Most of the populations are in the northern Sacramento Valley. There are currently five known populations in Sacramento County; two of these are on Mather Field.

This vernal pool endemic plant prefers areas of low competition and minor disturbance. It occurs most often on the prior year's gopher mounds along the margins of vernal pools.

Boggs Lake Hedge-hyssop

MAR- MAY
1-3 INCHES
ENDANGERED

Gratiola heterosepala

Listed as endangered under the California Endangered Species Act.

This tiny vernal pool endemic is known from vernal pools and other seasonal wetlands. There are several occurrences in Sacramento County including one on Mather Field.

This plant is very short-lived and also prefers areas of low competition. It germinates when the water warms and begins to recede. It blooms within a week or two, self-pollinates, and then sets seed. Once the seeds have matured, it quickly drops them, and the whole plant disintegrates.

RARE

Photo by Jennifer Hogan.

Photo by John Game.

Legenere

Legenere limosa

APR-JUN
3-12 INCHES
RARE

Considered rare and endangered throughout its range by the California Native Plant Society.

Known from fewer that fifty locations within California, mostly in the lower Sacramento Valley. There are several occurrences on Mather Field.

This vernal pool endemic plant prefers the deeper and wetter vernal pools. The most common type is self-pollinating and does not have any petals. The second type is very uncommon and has white petals that re-semble a small Downingia (see page 31).

Sacramento Orcutt Grass

Orcuttia viscida

MAY-JUL
2-8 INCHES
ENDANGERED

Listed as endangered under the Federal and California Endangered Species Acts.

This unusual grass is entirely endemic to a few vernal pools in Sacramento County. There are only nine known occurrences. While not currently known to occur at Mather Field, it does occur only a short distance away.

Sacramento orcutt grass is a member of a small group of grasses, all of which are endemic to vernal pools. Each species produces a sticky, bitter, and acidic substance. Ecologists believe that this substance helps prevent insects from eating the plants.

R
A
R
E

Why should we care?

All living organisms have intrinsic value. But there are also practical reasons to conserve species. Every organism evolves to deal with certain sets of environmental pressures, leading to unique physical or chemical adaptations. Most medicinal drugs originated as a chemical compound produced by plants or animals. If we allow a species to go extinct, we will never know if it might have been the source of a new wonder drug.

FERNS & FERN ALLIES

Isoeteaceae - Quillwort Family

Isoetes howellii	Howell's quillwort	vernal pools, marshes
Isoetes orcuttii	Orcutt's quillwort	vernal pools

Marsileaceae - Marsilea Family

Marsilea vestita ssp. *v.*	Hairy pepperwort	vernal pools, streams
Pilularia americana	American pillwort	vernal pools

DICOTS

Apiaceae - Carrot Family

*Conium maculatum**	Poison hemlock	marshes
Eryngium castrense	Coyote thistle	vernal pools
Lomatium caruifolium var. *c.*	Caraway-leaved lomatium	grassland
Sanicula bipinnatifida	Purple sanicle	grassland

Asclepiadaceae - Milkweed Family

Asclepias fascicularis	Narrow-leaf milkweed	grassland

Asteraceae - Sunflower Family

Achyrachaena mollis	Blow wives	grassland
Baccharis pilularis	Coyote bush	grassland
Blennosperma nanum var. *n.*	Yellow carpet	vernal pool margins
*Carduus pycnocephalus**	Italian thistle	grassland, disturbed
*Centaurea solstitialis**	Yellow starthistle	grassland, disturbed
*Chamomilla suaveolens**	Pineapple weed	disturbed areas
*Filago gallica**	Filago	disturbed areas
Grindelia camporum var. *c.*	Gum plant	grassland
Hemizonia fitchii	Fitch's tarweed	vernal pools, grassland
Heterotheca grandiflora	Telegraph weed	disturbed areas
Holocarpha virgata	Twiggy tarweed	grassland
*Hypochaeris glabra**	Smooth cat's-ear	vernal pool margins
*Hypochaeris radicata**	Rough cat's-ear	grassland
*Lactuca serriola**	Prickly lettuce	grassland
Lasthenia californica	California goldfields	grassland
Lasthenia fremontii	Vernal pool goldfields	vernal pools
Lasthenia glaberrima	Rayless goldfields	vernal pools
Layia fremontii	Fremont's tidy-tips	grassland
*Leontodon taraxacoides**	Hawkbit	vernal pools
Madia elegans ssp. *vernalis*	Spring madia	grassland
Micropus californicus var. *c.*	Q Tips	grassland
Microseris douglasii ssp. *tenella*	Douglas' microseris	grassland
Psilocarphus brevissimus var. *b.*	Woolly marbles	vernal pools
Psilocarphus oregonus	Oregon woolly marbles	pools, grassland
Psilocarphus tenellus var. *globiferus*	Slender woolly marbles	vernal pools
*Silybum marianum**	Milk thistle	grassland, disturbed
*Soliva sessilis**	Soliva	grassland, disturbed
Sonchus asper ssp. *a.**	Sow thistle	grassland, disturbed

L I S T

* non-native

Asteraceae (continued)

*Tragopogon sp.**	Salsify	grassland
Wyethia angustifolia	Mule's-ear	grassland
Xanthium strumarium	Cocklebur	disturbed

Boraginaceae - Borage Family

Amsinckia menziesii var. *intermedia*	Fiddleneck	grassland, disturbed
Plagiobothrys bracteatus	Smooth popcorn flower	vernal pools
Plagiobothrys fulvus	Field popcorn flower	grassland
Plagiobothrys greenei	Greene's popcorn flower	pool margins
Plagiobothrys leptocladus	Prostrate popcorn flower	vernal pools
Plagiobothrys stipitatus var. *micranthus*	Slender popcorn flower	vernal pools

Brassicaceae - Mustard Family

*Brassica nigra**	Black mustard	grassland, disturbed
Cardamine oligosperma	Western bittercress	vernal pools
*Hirschfeldia incana**	Field mustard	grassland
Lepidium latipes var. *l.*	Dwarf peppergrass	grassland
Lepidium nitidum var. *n.*	Shining peppergrass	vernal pool margins
*Raphanus raphanistrum**	Jointed wild radish	grassland, disturbed
*Raphanus sativus**	Common wild radish	grassland, disturbed
Rorippa nasturtium-aquaticum	Water-cress	marshes
Thysanocarpus radians	Spokepod	grassland

Callitrichaceae - Water Starwort Family

Callitriche marginata	Winged water starwort	vernal pools

Campanulaceae - Bellflower Family

Downingia bicornuta var. *picta*	Horned downingia	vernal pools
Downingia cuspidata	Toothed downingia	vernal pools
Downingia ornatissima var. *o.*	Folded downingia	vernal pools
Legenere limosa	Legenere	vernal pools

Caryophyllaceae - Pink Family

*Cerastium glomeratum**	Mouse-ear chickweed	grassland
Sagina decumbens ssp. *occidentalis*	Western pearlwort	vernal pool margins
*Spergularia bocconei**	Boccon's sand-spurrey	disturbed areas

Convolvulaceae - Morning-Glory Family

*Convolvulus arvensis**	Bindweed	grassland
Cuscuta howelliana	Vernal pool dodder	vernal pools

Crassulaceae - Stonecrop Family

Crassula aquatica	Water pygmy-weed	vernal pools
*Crassula tillaea**	Moss pygmy-weed	disturbed areas

Elatinaceae - Waterwort Family

Elatine californica	California waterwort	vernal pools
Elatine rubella	Red waterwort	vernal pools

LIST

* non-native

Vernal Pools of Mather Field

Euphorbiaceae - Spurge Family
Eremocarpus setigerus   Turkey mullein, dove weed   grassland

Fabaceae - Pea Family
Lathyrus hirsutus*	Hairy pea	grassland
Lotus micranthus	Smallflower lotus	grassland, disturbed
Lotus purshianus var. *p.*	Spanish lotus	grassland
Lupinus bicolor	Miniature lupine	grassland
Medicago polymorpha*	Bur clover	grassland, vernal pools
Trifolium depauperatum var. *d.*	Dwarf sack clover	vernal pools, grassland
Trifolium depauperatum var. *truncatum*	Pale sack clover	vernal pools, grassland
Trifolium dubium*	Hop clover	grassland
Trifolium hirtum*	Rose clover	grassland, disturbed
Trifolium repens*	White lawn clover	vernal pool margins
Trifolium variegatum	White-tipped clover	vernal pools
Vicia sativa ssp. *nigra**	Common vetch	grassland, disturbed
Vicia villosa ssp. *v.**	Winter vetch	grassland, disturbed

Fagaceae - Oak Family
Quercus douglasii	Blue oak	grassland
Quercus lobata	Valley oak	grassland
Quercus wislizeni	Interior live oak	grassland

Gentianaceae - Gentian Family
| *Centaurium muehlenbergii* | June centaury | vernal pool margins |
| *Cicendia quadrangularis* | Cicendia | vernal pool margins |

Geraniaceae - Geranium Family
Erodium botrys*	Filaree	grassland
Erodium cicutarium*	Cut-leaf filaree	grassland
Geranium carolinianum	Carolina geranium	grassland
Geranium dissectum*	Cut-leaf geranium	mesic areas

Hypericaceae - St. John's Wort Family
Hypericum perforatum*   Klamath weed   grassland, disturbed

Lamiaceae - Mint Family
Mentha pulegium*	Pennyroyal	marshes
Pogogyne douglasii	Douglas' beard-style	vernal pools
Pogogyne zizyphoroides	Sacramento beard-style	vernal pools
Trichostema lanceolatum	Vinegar weed	grassland, vernal pools

Limnanthaceae - Meadowfoam Family
Limnanthes alba ssp. *a.*   White meadowfoam   vernal pool margins

Lythraceae - Loosestrife Family
Lythrum hyssopifolia*   Hyssop loosestrife   vernal pools

* non-native

Malvaceae - Mallow Family
   Sidalcea calycosa ssp. *c.*   Vernal pool checkerbloom   vernal pools
   Sidalcea hirsuta   Alkali checkerbloom   grassland

Molluginaceae - Carpet-Weed Family
   *Mollugo verticillata**   Carpet-weed   disturbed areas

Myrtaceae - Myrtle Family
   *Eucalyptus globulus**   Blue gum   planted

Onagraceae - Evening-Primrose Family
   Epilobium brachycarpum   Willow-herb   disturbed areas
   Epilobium pygmaeum   Smooth boisduvalia   vernal pool margins
   Epilobium torreyi   Soft boisduvalia   vernal pool margins
   Ludwigia peploides ssp. *p.*   Yellow waterweed   lake, marshes

Papaveraceae - Poppy Family
   Eschscholzia californica   California poppy   grassland
   Eschscholzia lobbii   Frying pan poppy   grassland

Plantaginaceae - Plantain Family
   *Plantago coronopus**   Fern-leaf plantain   disturbed areas
   Plantago erecta   Dwarf plantain   grassland
   *Plantago lanceolata**   English plantain   disturbed areas

Polemoniaceae - Phlox Family
   Navarretia intertexta ssp. *i.*   Spiny navarretia   vernal pool margins
   Navarretia leucocephala ssp. *l.*   White navarretia   vernal pools

Polygonaceae - Buckwheat Family
   Eriogonum nudum var. *n.*   Nude buckwheat   grassland
   *Polygonum arenastrum**   Common knotweed   disturbed areas
   *Polygonum persicaria**   Lady's thumb bistort   marshes
   Polygonum punctatum   Dotted smartweed   marshes
   *Rumex acetosella**   Sheep sorrel   grassland
   *Rumex conglomeratus**   Clustered dock   vernal pools, marshes
   *Rumex crispus**   Curly dock   vernal pools, marshes
   *Rumex pulcher**   Fiddle dock   vernal pools, marshes

Portulacaceae - Purslane Family
   Calandrinia ciliata   Red maids   grassland, disturbed
   Montia fontana   Water chickweed, blinks   vernal pools

Primulaceae - Primrose Family
   *Anagallis arvensis**   Scarlet pimpernel   grassland, disturbed
   Centunculus minimus   Chaffweed   vernal pools

Ranunculaceae - Buttercup Family
   Ranunculus aquatilis var. *capillaceus*   Water buttercup   vernal pools, marshes

* non-native

LIST

Ranunculaceae (continued)

Ranunculus bonariensis var. *trisepalus*	Vernal pool buttercup	vernal pools
*Ranunculus muricatus**	Spiny fruit buttercup	wet areas

Rubiaceae - Madder Family

Galium aparine	Common bedstraw	grassland, disturbed
*Galium parisiense**	Wall bedstraw	grassland

Salicaceae - Willow Family

Populus fremontii ssp. *f.*	Fremont's cottonwood	lakeside
Salix exigua	Sandbar willow	lakeside
Salix lasiolepis	Arroyo willow	lakeside

Scrophulariaceae - Figwort Family

Castilleja attenuata	Valley tassels	grassland
Castilleja campestris ssp. *c.*	Field owl's clover	vernal pools
Gratiola ebracteata	Bractless hedge-hyssop	vernal pools
Gratiola heterosepala	Boggs Lake hedge-hyssop	vernal pools
Mimulus guttatus	Seep spring monkeyflower	marshes
Mimulus tricolor	Vernal pool monkeyflower	vernal pools
Triphysaria eriantha ssp. *e.*	Johnny-tuck, butter&eggs	grassland
Triphysaria pusilla	Little owl's clover	grassland
Veronica peregrina ssp. *xalapensis*	Purslane speedwell	vernal pools

MONOCOTS

Alismataceae - Water-Plantain Family

Alisma plantago-aquatica	Water-plantain	marshes
Damasonium californicum	Fringed water-plantain	vernal pools

Cyperaceae - Sedge Family

*Cyperus difformis**	Variable flatsedge	marshes
Cyperus eragrostis	Tall flatsedge	marshes
Eleocharis acicularis var. *a.*	Dwarf spikerush	vernal pools
Eleocharis macrostachya	Pale spikerush	marshes, vernal pools
Scirpus acutus var. *occidentalis*	Tule	marshes

Juncaceae - Rush Family

Juncus acuminatus	Tapertip rush	marshes
Juncus balticus	Baltic rush	marshes
Juncus bufonius var. *occidentalis*	Toad rush	vernal pool margins
*Juncus capitatus**	Capped dwarf rush	vernal pool margins
Juncus effusus var. *pacificus*	Pacific rush	marshes
Juncus leiospermus var. *ahartii*	Ahart's dwarf rush	vernal pools
Juncus oxymeris	Pointed rush	marshes
Juncus tenuis	Soft rush	grassland
Juncus uncialis	Inch-high dwarf rush	vernal pools
Juncus xiphioides	Iris-leaved rush	marshes, vernal pools

L I S T

* non-native

Juncaginceae - Arrow-Grass Family
Lilaea scilloides — Flowering quillwort — vernal pools

Lemnaceae - Duckweed Family
Lemna minor — Small duckweed — summer water

Liliaceae - Lily Family

Allium amplectens	Wild onion	grassland
Brodiaea coronaria ssp. *c.*	Crown brodiaea	grassland
Brodiaea elegans ssp. *e.*	Elegant brodiaea	grassland
Brodiaea minor	Vernal pool brodiaea	vernal pools
Calochortus luteus	Gold nuggets	grassland
Chlorogalum pomeridianum var. *p.*	Soap root	grassland
Dichelostemma capitatum ssp. *c.*	Blue dicks	grassland
Dichelostemma multiflorum	Wild hyacinth	grassland
Triteleia hyacinthina	White hyacinth	grassland
Triteleia laxa	Wally baskets	grassland

Poaceae - Grass Family

*Aegilops triuncialis**	Barbed goatgrass	grassland
*Agrostis avenacea**	Bent grass	marshes
*Aira caryophyllea**	Silver hairgrass	grassland
Alopecurus saccatus	Meadow foxtail	vernal pools
Andropogon virginicus var. *v.**	Broomsedge bluestem	marshes
*Avena barbata**	Slender wild oats	grassland
*Avena fatua**	Wild oats	grassland
*Briza minor**	Little quaking grass	grassland
*Bromus diandrus**	Ripgut brome	grassland
*Bromus hordeaceus**	Soft chess brome	grassland
Deschampsia danthonioides	Vernal pool hairgrass	vernal pools
*Echinochloa crus-galli**	Barnyard grass	marshes
Elymus elymoides	Squirreltail grass	grassland
*Glyceria declinata**	Manna grass	vernal pools, marshes
Hordeum marinum ssp. *gussoneanum**	Mediterranean barley	grassland, pools
Hordeum murinum ssp. *leporinum**	Foxtail barley	grassland
Leptochloa mucronata	Sprangletop grass	marshes
*Lolium multiflorum**	Italian ryegrass	grassland, vernal pools
*Lolium perenne**	Perennial ryegrass	grassland
Nassella pulchra	Purple needlegrass	grassland
*Poa annua**	Annual bluegrass	grassland, vernal pools
*Polypogon monspeliensis**	Rabbit's foot grass	vernal pools, marshes
Scribneria bolanderi	Scribneria	vernal pool margins
*Taeniatherum caput-medusae**	Medusahead	grassland
*Vulpia bromoides**	Annual fescue	grassland
Vulpia microstachys var. *m.*	Desert fescue	grassland

Typhaceae - Cattail Family
Typha angustifolia — Narrow-leaved cattail — marshes
Typha latifolia — Broad-leaved cattail — marshes

LIST

Index

INDEX